IGINLA SPARKS THE FLAMES

MIKE LEONETTI

Illustrations by
GARY MCLAUGHLIN

SCHOLASTIC CANADA LTD.
Toronto New York London Auckland Sydney
Mexico City New Delhi Hong Kong Buenos Aires

Scholastic Canada Ltd.
604 King Street West, Toronto, Ontario M5V 1E1, Canada

Scholastic Inc.
557 Broadway, New York, NY 10012, USA

Scholastic Australia Pty Limited
PO Box 579, Gosford, NSW 2250, Australia

Scholastic New Zealand Limited
Private Bag 94407, Botany, Manukau 2163, New Zealand

Scholastic Children's Books
Euston House, 24 Eversholt Street, London NW1 1DB, UK

www.scholastic.ca

While some of the events described and some of the characters in this book may be based on actual historical events and real people, Riley and his family are fictional characters created by the author, and the story is a work of fiction.

The author referred to the following sources:
Newspapers: *Toronto Star, Toronto Sun, Globe and Mail*
Magazines: *Hockey News*, Maple Leafs Game Day Program of March 4, 2006.
Video: 2004 Stanley Cup video
Books: *The Sensational Jarome Iginla* by Peter Bailey, *Hockey's Hottest Players* by Arpon Basu.
Record Books: *NHL Official Guide & Record Book 2014*.
Websites: kidsport.ab.ca, hockey-reference.com, NHL.com.

Library and Archives Canada Cataloguing in Publication
Leonetti, Mike, 1958-, author
Iginla sparks the Flames / Mike Leonetti ; illustrated by Gary McLaughlin.

ISBN 978-1-4431-2873-5 (pbk.)

1. Iginla, Jarome, 1977- --Juvenile fiction. 2. Calgary Flames (Hockey team)--Juvenile fiction. I. McLaughlin, Gary, illustrator
II. Title.

PS8573.E58734I35 2014a   jC813'.54   C2014-901810-X

6 5 4 3 2 1   Printed in Malaysia 108   14 15 16 17 18

To all those who help manage, organize, sponsor and participate in the KidSport program all across Canada, and to Jarome Iginla for his efforts and contributions to KidSport.
— M.L.

To Tyler Ash, a great player at ten years old, and to his hockey parents, Jerry and Kristi, who help fuel his dreams.
— G.M.

"Hey, Riley," Dad called. "Uncle Zach is here. Get your skates and stick. We're ready to go."

We were going to the outdoor rink at Clearview Park to play some hockey on a Sunday afternoon. When we got there we chose sides and it was game on!

It was fun, but I really wanted to play hockey with a team. I knew that we didn't have money for extras, though. Could my dad afford it?

On the way home I asked Dad about joining a league in the fall.

"Riley, you know it's just me and you, and I have to work two jobs just to keep us in this house," he said.

Mom had moved back to Toronto, and Dad and I were on our own. I missed her, but my grandparents and uncles were nearby and helped out. I played baseball and soccer, but I really wanted to play hockey.

Uncle Zach saw the disappointment on my face. "There are organizations that help out kids who can't afford to play sports," he said. "Why don't we do some research?"

It wasn't long before I found KidSport. It looked like they might help with registration fees and maybe some equipment. Uncle Zach said he'd even drive me to their office in Calgary to apply in person.

"It's okay by me, Riley," Dad said, "but don't get your hopes too high."

I tried to stay cool, but I was excited that I might be able to play on a real team.

When we got to the office, Jarome Iginla of the Flames was signing autographs! I knew he donated money to KidSport every time he scored a goal in an NHL game, but I never expected to see him in person.

I explained why I was there. He showed me where the forms were and signed a T-shirt for me. I held on to it tightly. There were a lot of people there, but he never stopped smiling and he made me feel like I was important.

We filled in the papers and were set to leave when our car would not start. Jarome saw what happened and said we should stay overnight in Calgary while the car got repaired. He even paid for our hotel room. We left for home the next day but I would never forget how generous Jarome had been.

Now I knew why he was a hero to so many people.

I started to read as much as I could about Jarome. His parents had split up when he was young, and he lived with his mother. He started playing hockey when he was six but he loved lots of sports, like me. He was drafted in the first round by the Dallas Stars but was traded to Calgary before playing in a single game. Before too long he was a star right winger for the Flames.

Soon Jarome was one of the best in the NHL. He led the league in scoring in 2001–02, with 52 goals and 96 points. He could play a strong game and score goals from almost anywhere on the ice. The Flames named him team captain and he hoped to lead the team back to the playoffs.

Late that summer I heard from KidSport. They would pay my registration fee, and for some equipment. Mom had saved up to replace my worn-out skates, and Dad and my uncles pitched in. Soon I had everything I needed.

I went to a tryout and made the Royals team. I got the last roster spot, but I was on the squad and that was the most important thing. Making the team made me feel like I belonged to something special. I could hardly wait for my first game!

Since I was a right-handed shot, I was put on right wing, just like Jarome Iginla. Coach Tucker stressed putting my shot on net every time. I practised it every chance I could. It took a while, but I started to get better and soon I could come down the wing and blast a shot. I watched Jarome play and tried to copy his style, skating straight forward to the net. I wore the T-shirt Jarome signed for me underneath my team sweater for every game and practice.

Dad set up a small rink next to the garage as soon as it turned cold. He got up early to flood it before work. I practised my shot before school and at the end of the day, and Dad joined me when he could. He had been a good player when he was young, and I wanted to make him proud.

My best game came against the Bobcats. I scored both goals in a 2–0 win, with my family there to cheer me on. The win got us into the playoffs and Coach Tucker said, "You look more and more like Iginla out there, Riley. Keep up the good work!" I had a big smile on my face when I met my dad after the game.

The Royals won a couple of playoff games but the Tigers eventually beat us and our season was over. I was a much better player by the end of the year. And even though my team was out, I still hoped the Flames could win it all.

The Flames had gotten off to a slow start that season, but then they really came on. They ended up with 42 wins and 94 points to make the playoffs. Jarome scored 41 goals and tied with two others for the most goals that season.

Just before the playoffs began, a letter arrived from KidSport. Everyone in the program had been enrolled in a draw for playoff tickets, and I was one of the winners! I got a pair of tickets for a home game during the Stanley Cup finals.

"That's great, Riley," Dad said, "but the Flames have to beat three tough teams to get to the final. I doubt we'll be able to use those tickets."

"You never know, Dad. Just look how much Jarome has done so far," I said.

Sure enough, Calgary beat Vancouver in the first round and surprised Detroit before beating San Jose to make it to the finals against the Tampa Bay Lightning! The Flames won the first game but the Lightning beat them in the second to tie the series. The third game was going to be in Calgary and my Dad and I were going!

The Saddledome was full of red sweaters, so I fit right in. Nothing was going to stop Jarome that night. In the first period he got into a scrap with Lightning captain Vincent Lecavalier. In the second he set up the opening goal, getting the puck over to Chris Simon. The Flames made it 2–0 and Jarome made it 3–0 in the third, taking a beautiful pass from Robyn Regehr and putting it into the Lightning net.

Miikka Kiprusoff got the shutout for the Flames, who were suddenly just two wins away from their first Stanley Cup since 1989! I couldn't stop talking about it on the way home.

We watched the rest of the series on TV. Calgary went up 3–2 and had a chance to win the Cup on home ice in game six, but Martin St. Louis scored in overtime to beat them. The series went to seven games, and finally the Lightning took the Cup with a 2–1 win.

Jarome Iginla did everything possible for his team in the playoffs that year, including scoring 13 times, setting up goals for his teammates and being a leader. It just hadn't been enough this time — but he had proved that he was a great hockey player.

That summer Dad and I helped install new boards and glass at the Clearview Park rink. It was fun to work with our neighbours to make the rink a better place to play hockey the next winter.

"We're giving something back to the community, just like Jarome does," I said to Dad as we worked. "We should do something like this every year."

Next hockey season could not come soon enough, and I knew that my family was going to be there for me. I wanted them to be proud of everything I did, on and off the ice. Jarome Iginla had helped show me how.

ABOUT JAROME IGINLA

Jarome Iginla was born on July 1, 1977, in Edmonton, Alberta, and grew up in St. Albert with his mother. His father remained a prominent part of his life but lived in Edmonton. Iginla played minor hockey in St. Albert and major junior for the Kamloops Blazers in British Columbia, where he was a part of two Memorial Cup winning teams. In his final year of junior hockey, 1995–96, he scored 63 goals in 63 games.

The Dallas Stars drafted Iginla 11th overall in 1995, but he was traded to the Calgary Flames in December of 1995, in a deal that sent Joe Nieuwendyk to Dallas.

Iginla was Calgary's captain from 2003 until he was traded to the Pittsburgh Penguins and then signed with the Boston Bruins in 2013. As a member of the Flames, he scored 50 or more goals twice and was named to the NHL's All-Star Team four times. He was given the Ted Lindsay Award as the most outstanding player, as voted on by members of the NHL, for his performance in 2001–02. Iginla has won or shared the Maurice Richard Trophy for most goals during the regular season twice, and he scored 525 career goals as a Flame, the most in team history. In 1,219 games with Calgary, he recorded 1,095 points — also a team record. Iginla has won the King Clancy Memorial Trophy for his leadership qualities and humanitarian contributions.

Iginla has represented Canada many times, both as a junior player and as a professional. He was a member of the Canadian team that won the World Cup in September of 2004. He was also with Team Canada when they won the gold medal at the 2002 and 2010 Winter Olympics (setting up Sidney Crosby's "Golden Goal" in 2010).

ABOUT KIDSPORT

KidSport is a non-profit organization with local chapters all across Canada. It is focused on providing positive sport opportunities to children from low-income families. With the help of community supporters, KidSport is able to assist local kids by subsidizing sport registration fees and certain sport equipment for qualified applicants so kids can play their chosen sport safely and confidently.